Spelling and Vocabulary Skills

Level 2

Blackline Masters

A Division of The McGraw·Hill Companies

Columbus, Ohio

www.sra4kids.com

SRA/McGraw-Hill

A Division of The McGraw·Hill Companies

Send all inquiries to:
SRA/McGraw-Hill
8787 Orion Place
Columbus, OH 43240-4027

Printed in the United States of America.

ISBN 0-07-571101-X

3 4 5 6 7 8 9 POH 07 06 05 04

Table of Contents

Unit 6   Our Country and Its People

▶Vocabulary Strategies

 As you read a story, you may see words you do not understand. There are many ways to figure out the meaning of words.

1. Finally he said, "This is your last *chance*. If you don't say pigs, I'm leaving."

Can you figure out the meaning of the word *chance* from the sentence around it?

2. The Ant *leaned* back.

Can you figure out the meaning of the word *leaned* by looking for another word within the word?

3. Once upon a time, there were three little *figs*.

Sometimes, the best way to learn the meaning of a word is to look it up in a dictionary.

Think of one sentence using *fig*, one using *leaned*, and one using *chance*. Be ready to share your sentences with the class.

▶**Vocabulary Strategies**

VOCABULARY

Practice

Circle the correct word for each sentence. Even though you don't know the meaning of the word, you may be able to figure out the correct answer.

4. Yesterday, Anna   grows   finds   her kitty around the house.   chased

5. A kiwi is a small   green   hippo   fruit.   large

6. A pteranodon was a   car   tomato   dinosaur.   flying

7. I love to fly in a   river   blimp.   potato

8. I am going to go   skating   crawled   tomorrow.   skipped

▶ The *gl, bl,* and *pl* Blends

Word List

1. plus
2. glue
3. blink
4. plot
5. glad
6. blend

Selection Words

7. plan
8. block
9. plum
10. blast

Pattern Study

Look at the spelling patterns:

gl   bl   pl

The sounds of these letters often combine at the beginnings of words. We say these two sounds quickly without any space between them.

▶Write the words that begin with the same sounds as *glass*.

1. _____   2. _____

▶Write the words that begin with the same sounds as *blue*.

3. _____   5. _____

4. _____   6. _____

▶Write the words that begin with the same sounds as *play*.

7. _____   9. _____

8. _____   10. _____

UNIT I Sharing Stories • **Lesson I** *Ant and the Three Little Figs*

▶The *gl, bl,* and *pl* **Blends**

Strategies

Visualization Strategy Circle the correct spelling for each word. Then write the correct word.

11. plan   plann   _____

12. blok   block   _____

13. gluw   glue   _____

14. blink   blick   _____

15. plot   plott   _____

16. pluss   plus   _____

Meaning Strategy Write the spelling word that best fits the sentence.

17. A _____ is a tasty purple fruit.

18. Pink is a _____ of red and white.

19. I am not sad, but I am _____.

20. The _____ from the explosion was loud.

SPELLING

Name _____ Date _____

▶Context Clues

You can learn a lot about the meaning of a
word from the words and sentences around it.
Remember to
▶ look for words that mean the same thing
▶ look for words that have the opposite
  meaning
▶ look for words that explain
▶ look for words that describe

 **Look at these sentences and answer the
questions about the underlined word.**

1. Juan's kite was stuck high in a tree, so he
began to <u>yank</u> and pull sharply at the string.

Ask yourself, "What did Juan do to the string?"

_____

Yank must mean _____.

2. The <u>stallion</u> was a horse named Terry, but he
was not a female horse.

Ask yourself, "What is the opposite of female?"

_____

Stallion must mean _____ horse.

▶**Context Clues**

Practice

Circle the closest meaning to the underlined word. You may not know the word, but you still may be able to figure out the correct answer using context clues.

3. The <u>United</u> States are all 50 states together.
   a. far apart   c. fighting
   b. tiny   d. joined

4. There were so many people, I lost her in the <u>crowd</u>.
   a. many people   c. no dogs
   b. some people   d. no people

5. The gorilla won't drop her baby. She will <u>clutch</u> it to her chest.
   a. pay money   c. throw
   b. hold tightly   d. flip

6. The <u>moat</u> at the king's castle was deep. Many fish and ducks lived there.
   a. large boat on an island   c. tower on a castle
   b. water around a castle   d. birdbath on an island

7. Do you get up at <u>dawn</u>, or do you like to sleep later?
   a. midnight   c. just before evening
   b. first light of day d. grassy place

VOCABULARY

▶ The *gr, dr,* and *tr* Blends

Word List

1. drip

2. drum

3. gray

4. grin

5. tree

6. trip

Selection Words

7. grow

8. truck

9. try

10. dress

Pattern Study

Look at the patterns:

gr   dr   tr

The sounds of these letters often combine at the beginnings of words. We say the two sounds quickly without any space between them.

▶ Write the words that begin with the same sound as *grape*.

1. _____ 2. _____ 3. _____

▶ Write the words that begin with the same sound as *dry*.

4. _____ 5. _____ 6. _____

▶ Write the words that begin with the same sound as *trap*.

7. _____   9. _____

8. _____   10. _____

Name _____ Date _____

▶ **The *gr*, *dr*, and *tr* Blends**

Strategies

Visualization Strategy Add the blends to the letters on the right to form a spelling word. The first one is done for you.

11. *gr*   ay   gray

12. *tr*   ee   _____

13. *gr*   in   _____

14. *dr*   ess   _____

15. *gr*   ow   _____

16. *dr*   um   _____

Vowel-Substitution Strategy Replace the underlined vowel with the new vowel. Then write the new word.

17. dr<u>o</u>p + *i* = drip

18. tr<u>a</u>ck + *u* = _____

19. tr<u>a</u>p + *i* = _____

20. gr<u>e</u>w + *o* = _____

SPELLING

UNIT 1 **Sharing Stories • Lesson 3** *The Library*

▶Word Structure

You may be able to learn something about a word by breaking it into its different parts.

▶ Look for words inside the word.
▶ Look for a prefix at the beginning of the word.
▶ Look for a suffix at the end of the word.

Try It!

1. My aunt's house is orange and purple. I think she should <u>redecorate</u>.

   re- is a prefix that means "again."

   What does the word *redecorate* mean? _____

2. I was afraid, but the doctor's shot was <u>painless</u>.

   -less is a suffix that means "without."

   What does the word *painless* mean? _____

3. A <u>nearsighted</u> student was reading in the library.

   What does the word *nearsighted* mean? _____

Word Structure • Spelling and Vocabulary Skills

▶**Word Structure**

Practice

Write the correct word in the blank. You may not know the word, but you can figure out the correct answer using *word structure*.

4. It is hard for Grandmother to read because

she is _____.

farsighted   farfetched   insighted

5. The detective was _____, and could not
solve the case.

clueless   clues   fearless

6. My parents called me Jeremiah Jethro Jacob Johnson,

Junior. I want them to _____ me.

refry   renew   rename

7. The project is to teach pigs to fly. I think

it is _____.

hopeful   hopeless   hoping

8. The judge worked at the _____.

courthouse   doghouse   birdhouse

VOCABULARY

UNIT 1 **Sharing Stories • Lesson 3** *The Library*

▶ The Final /k/ Sound

Word List

1. park

2. kick

3. bark

4. dark

5. stick

6. hook

7. track

Selection Words

8. book

9. took

10. stack

Pattern Study

Look at the patterns:

k   ck

These letters often spell the /k/ sound at the ends of words.

▶ For each group of words, write the words in ABC order and circle the letter or letters that spell the final /k/ sound.

park   bark   dark

1. _____   2. _____   3. _____

stack   kick   stick   track

4. _____   6. _____

5. _____   7. _____

book   took   hook

8. _____

9. _____

10. _____

The Final /k/ Sound • **Spelling and Vocabulary Skills**

UNIT 1 **Sharing Stories • Lesson 3** *The Library*

▶**The Final /k/ Sound**

Strategies

 Proofreading Strategy Circle the four spelling mistakes in the story, then write the misspelled words correctly on the lines.

Andrew Carnegie gave money to build over 2,500 libraries all over the country, many with a parck. He helped put us on the trak to becoming good readers. I think we should thank him for every boock we toock from the library.

11. _____   13. _____

12. _____   14. _____

 Meaning Strategy Write in words to complete the sentences below. Use *dark, kick, hook, bark,* or *stick.*

15. It was hard to find my fishing _____.

16. It was late and getting _____.

17. Throw the _____ to the dog.

18. Then the dog will not _____.

19. _____ the soccer ball into the net.

▶Dictionary

> When you are unable to learn something about a word from the context of the story, or by breaking it into different parts, a dictionary may help.

 **Try It!**

Everyone looked at her in *amazement*.

Can you learn the meaning of *amazement*

from context clues? _____

How about from word structure? _____

A glossary is the part of a book that gives the meaning of some words you find in that book. A glossary is a kind of dictionary.

Your teacher will help you to look up the word *amazement* in the Glossary of the ***Open Court Reading, Level Two, Unit One Anthology.***

What does *amazement* mean?

_____

Name _____ Date _____

▶**Dictionary**

VOCABULARY

Practice

	bird / brown
bird /bûrd/ *n.* an animal that has wings, two legs, and a body covered with feathers. **birthday** /bûrth´dā/ *n.* **1.** the day on which a person is born. **2.** the return each year of this day. **bite** /bīt/ *v.* **bit, bit ten,** or **bit, bit ing. 1.** to seize, cut into, or pierce with the teeth. **2.** to	wound with teeth, fangs, or a stinger. **bottle** /bot´əl/ *n.* a container, usually made of glass or plastic, which holds liquids. –*v.* **bot tled bot tling.** to put in bottles. **boy** /boi/ *n.* a very young male child. **brainstorm** /brān´storm/ *n.* a sudden bright idea; inspiration.

1. The *entry word* is the word you look up. Entry words are in ABC order.

   What is the first entry word on this page?

   _____

2. At the top of each dictionary page are two words called *guide words*. These are the first and last entry words on that page. Guide words help you to find an entry quickly.

   What are the guide words on this page?

   _____   _____

3. A *definition* is the meaning of a word. One or more definitions are given for each entry word. If there is more than one meaning, the definitions are numbered.

   What is the definition of *boy?*

   _____

▶ The *nd* and *st* Blends

Pattern Study

Word List

1. hand
2. land
3. pond
4. fast
5. lost
6. just

Selection Words

7. stand
8. stuck
9. story
10. spend

Look at the patterns:

st   nd

st is found at the beginnings and ends of words

nd is found at the end or middle of words, never at the beginning

▶Write the spelling words that begin with the same sounds as *stop*.

1. _____   2. _____   3. _____

▶Write the spelling words that end with the same sounds as *sand*.

4. _____   7. _____

5. _____   8. _____

6. _____

▶Write the spelling words that end with the same sounds as *most*.

9. _____   11. _____

10. _____

UNIT 1 **Sharing Stories • Lesson 4** *Story Hour—Starring Megan!*

▶The *nd* and *st* Blends

Strategies

 Visualization Strategy Circle the correct spelling for each word. Write the correct spelling on the line.

12. stuc   stuck   _____

13. pond   ponde   _____

14. storey   story   _____

Rhyming Strategy Write the spelling words that rhyme with the words below.

sand   and   band

15. _____

16. _____

17. _____

past   mast   cast

18. _____

mend   end   lend

19. _____

SPELLING

▶Thesaurus

A *thesaurus* is a book of synonyms.
A *synonym* is a word that means the same
or nearly the same as another word.

 **A synonym for *mad* is *furious*.**

1. Can you think of another synonym for *mad?*

_____

2. Can you think of a synonym for *happy?* _____

3. In "Tomás and the Library Lady," the wind was
howling. Some synonyms for *howling* are
moaning, *yowling*, *crying*, and *wailing*.

Can you figure out what *howling* means from

the meanings of these synonyms? _____

Remember that synonyms do not always have
exactly the same meaning, but are words that
are close in meaning.

UNIT 1 **Sharing Stories • Lesson 5** *Tomás and the Library Lady*

▶**Thesaurus**

VOCABULARY

Practice

Here is a sample page from a thesaurus.

Hot		**Hug**
hot	*adj.*	baking, boiling, burning, fiery, searing
hue	*n.*	color, shade, tint
hug	*v.*	clasp, hold, press, squeeze

4. How is a thesaurus like a dictionary? _____

_____

5. What is a synonym for <u>hot</u>? _____

_____

6. What is a synonym for <u>hue</u>? _____

_____

7. What is a synonym for <u>hug</u>? _____

_____

▶ Review

Word List

1. trick
2. blind
3. sock
4. blue
5. pest
6. walk

Selection Words

7. drink
8. black
9. desk
10. check

Pattern Study

Look at the patterns:

bl   **ck**   **k**   **st**

▶ Write the spelling pattern that completes the words. Then rewrite the words.

1. ____ue   _____

2. ____ind   _____

3. ____ack   _____

4. tri____   _____

5. so____   _____

6. pe____   _____

7. che____   _____

8. wal____   _____

9. drin____   _____

10. des____   _____

UNIT 1 **Sharing Stories • Lesson 5** *Tomás and the Library Lady*

▶**Review**

Strategies

 Rhyming Strategy Write the spelling word that rhymes with the words below.

11. rock   dock   _____

12. talk   chalk   _____

13. deck   neck   _____

14. nest   best   _____

 Vowel-Substitution Strategy Replace the underlined vowel with the new vowel. Then write the new word. The first one is done for you.

15. bl<u>e</u>nd + i = blind

16. bl<u>o</u>ck + a = _____

17. tr<u>a</u>ck + i = _____

18. d<u>i</u>sk + e = _____

19. dr<u>a</u>nk + i = _____

SPELLING

Name _____ Date _____

▶Base Word Families

A **base word** is a word that can stand alone. It will give you a clue to the meaning of other words in its family.

Base Word	Base Word Family Members
sun	sunny
	sunshine

 **Write the base word for each group below. The first one is done for you.**

1. peeking, peeked   peek

2. roomy, rooms   _____

3. stopped, stops   _____

4. moving, moved   _____

5. pleasing, pleased   _____

6. nearly, nearby   _____

7. eating, eaten   _____

8. cloudy, clouds   _____

9. brightly, brighter   _____

10. merrily, merrier   _____

►**Base Word Families**

Practice

Circle the words in the same base word family. Then write the base word and the meaning the words in this family share. The first one is done for you.

11. dashed   dusting   dashing

Base Word: dash   Meaning: run quickly

12. grass   grasses   gassed

Base Word: _____   Meaning: _____

13. jammed   jumped   jamming

Base Word: _____   Meaning: _____

14. mapped   mops   mapping

Base Word: _____   Meaning: _____

15. crashes   cashed   cashes

Base Word: _____   Meaning: _____

16. ants   anthill   attic

Base Word: _____   Meaning: _____

VOCABULARY

UNIT 2 Kindness • **Lesson 1** *Mushroom in the Rain*

▶The /a/ Sound

Word List

1. dash

2. gas

3. jam

4. map

5. cash

6. path

Selection Words

7. sat

8. ran

9. ant

10. had

Pattern Study

Look at the patterns:

m**a**sh   t**a**p

Say each word and listen for the middle sound. Both words contain the /a/ sound. *Mash* has a **consonant-vowel-consonant-consonant** pattern.
Tap has a **consonant-vowel-consonant** pattern.

▶Write the spelling words with the same pattern as *tap*.

1. _____   4. _____

2. _____   5. _____

3. _____   6. _____

▶Write the spelling words with the same pattern as *mash*.

7. _____   9. _____

8. _____

UNIT 2 Kindness • **Lesson I** *Mushroom in the Rain*

▶**The /a/ Sound**

SPELLING

Strategies

 Rhyming Strategy Write the spelling word that rhymes with each set of words below. The new word will have the same spelling pattern for /a/. The first one is done for you.

10. ham   ram   jam

11. dash   rash   _____

12. lap   cap   _____

13. bath   math   _____

14. tan   van   _____

 Visualization Strategy Circle the correct spelling for each word.

15. dash   desh

16. ges   gas

17. sat   sot

18. ant   ent

19. hud   had

UNIT 2 Kindness • **Lesson 2** *The Elves and the Shoemaker*

▶Homophones

A **homophone** is a word that sounds the same as another word but has a different spelling and meaning.

The <u>road</u> went through Concord.

Paul Revere <u>rode</u> a horse through Concord.

Road means *street.*   *Rode* means *did ride.*

 **Complete the sentences using *close* or *clothes*. Write the meaning of the word.**

Clothes means "what you wear."   *Close* means "shut."

1. Please _____ the door.

   _____ means _____.

2. It is cold. Wear warm _____ outside.

   _____ means _____.

Complete the sentence using *eye* or *I*. Write the meaning of the word.

Eye means "what you see with."   *I* means "myself."

3. _____ wanted to go to the zoo.

   _____ means _____.

Homophones • Spelling and Vocabulary Skills

UNIT 2 Kindness • **Lesson 2** *The Elves and the Shoemaker*

▶**Homophones**

Practice

Use these homophones to complete the sentences.

sun	read	hour	toe	blew
son	red	our	tow	blue

4. My brother and I walked _____ dog.

5. The wind _____ the kite.

6. Our class _____ a chapter book this week.

7. A nephew is the _____ of a brother or sister.

8. I hit my _____ on the diving board.

9. The huge, yellow _____ rose in the sky.

10. Sixty minutes is an _____.

11. Dalmatians rode on the _____ fire truck.

12. The airplane raced across the _____ sky.

13. A broken car may need a _____.

VOCABULARY

UNIT 2 Kindness • **Lesson 2** *The Elves and the Shoemaker*

▶ The /e/ Sound

Word List

1. bell
2. fed
3. nest
4. send
5. test
6. yet

Selection Words

7. went
8. then
9. next
10. them

Pattern Study

Look at the patterns:

b<u>e</u>st   l<u>e</u>d   sp<u>e</u>d

Say each word and listen for the middle sound. These words contain the /e/ sound.

▶Write the spelling words with the /e/ sound spelled with the **consonant-vowel-consonant** pattern.

1. _____ 2. _____

▶Write the spelling words with the /e/ sound spelled with the **consonant-vowel-consonant-consonant** pattern.

3. _____ 6. _____

4. _____ 7. _____

5. _____ 8. _____

▶Write the spelling words with the /e/ sound spelled with the **consonant-consonant-vowel-consonant** pattern.

9. _____ 10. _____

UNIT 2 Kindness • **Lesson 2** *The Elves and the Shoemaker*

▶**The /e/ Sound**

Strategies

Pronunciation Strategy Write the spelling word with the same vowel spelling pattern as each set of words below. Circle the letter that spells the /e/ sound in each answer.

11. rest   best _____

12. west   pest _____

13. well   fell _____

14. led   bed _____

15. bet   get _____

Proofreading Strategy Circle the misspelled words. Rewrite the words correctly below.

The customer wint on his way. The naxt morning the shoemaker woke up. Thon he saw more new shoes and was happy about tham. He and his wife were so happy that they would sind the elves away with presents.

16. _____   **19.** _____

17. _____   **20.** _____

18. _____

UNIT 2 Kindness • **Lesson 3** *The Paper Crane*

▶ Levels of Specificity
Categories

A category is a group of similar things. A word map can help you to put words into categories.

things that make music

types of drums

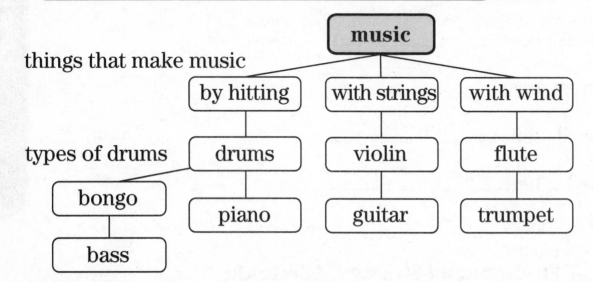

Try It! **Into what category would you place the word *crane*? Can you think of other ways to categorize *crane*? Complete the word map below.**

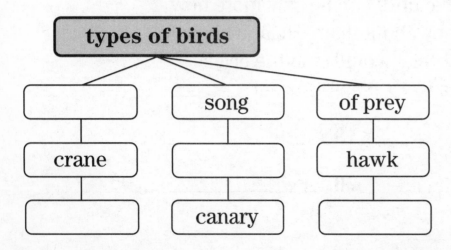

Categories • Spelling and Vocabulary Skills

Name _____ Date _____

▶ **Levels of Specificity Categories**

Practice

Into what category would you place the word *king*? Can you think of other ways to categorize *king*? Complete the word map below.

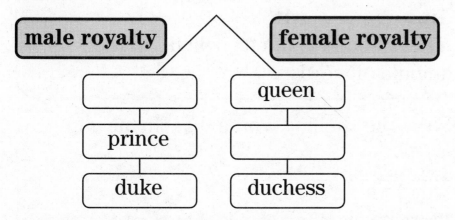

male royalty   female royalty

queen

prince

duke   duchess

Refer to the completed word map to answer the questions below.

1. Is a prince male or female? _____

2. Is a duchess male or female? _____

3. How are a king and queen alike? _____

_____

4. How are a king and queen different? _____

_____

5. How are a queen and duchess alike? _____

_____

VOCABULARY

UNIT 2 **Kindness • Lesson 3** *The Paper Crane*

► The /i/ Sound

Word List

1. win

2. fix

3. mix

4. pin

5. rip

6. zip

Selection Words

7. sit

8. his

9. this

10. lips

Pattern Study

Look at the pattern:

f**i**g   w**i**t

The /i/ sound is often spelled *i* in the middle of words.

► Write the spelling words that rhyme with *fin*.

1. _____   2. _____

► Write the spelling words that rhyme with *six*.

3. _____   4. _____

► Write the spelling words that rhyme with *dip*.

5. _____   6. _____

► Which other words have the **consonant-vowel-consonant** pattern?

7. _____   8. _____

► Which other words have the /i/ sound?

9. _____   10. _____

UNIT 2 Kindness • **Lesson 3** *The Paper Crane*

▶**The /i/ Sound**

Strategies

Rhyming Strategy Write the spelling word that rhymes with each set of words below. They will have the same spelling pattern for /i/.

11. pin   bin   _____

12. sip   zip   _____

13. wit   kit   _____

14. tin   win   _____

15. tips   dips   _____

Consonant-Substitution Strategy Replace the underlined letter to create a spelling word. Then write the new word. The first one is done for you.

16. fi<u>t</u> + x = fix

17. hi<u>m</u> + s = _____

18. <u>t</u>ip + z = _____

19. <u>f</u>ix + m = _____

20. thi<u>n</u> + s = _____

Exceptions

/i/ is sometimes spelled **vowel-consonant-e** as in *give* and *live*.

Name _____ Date _____

▶Multiple Meanings

Some words have **multiple meanings.** To figure out the meaning of the word that best fits the sentence, use context clues or a dictionary.

rose may mean: past tense of *rise*
fly   may mean: to move through the air
felt may mean: past tense of *feel*

 **Read these sentences from "Butterfly House." Write the meaning of the underlined word. Then write another meaning for the word. Use a dictionary if you need to.**

1. She <u>rose</u>, then rested on the fig tree branch.

Rose means _____.

Rose also may mean: _____.

2. I saw it <u>fly</u>.

Fly means _____.

Fly also may mean: _____.

3. She <u>felt</u> the first warm touch of the sun.

Felt means _____.

Felt also may mean: _____.

▶ **Multiple Meanings**

VOCABULARY

Practice

Read the different meanings for each word below. Write the meaning of the word as it is used in the sentence.

bank:	a place where money is kept	the side of a river or creek
foot:	the end part of a leg	twelve inches
bark:	short, loud sound a dog makes	outer covering of a tree

4. Manuel kept his money at the <u>bank</u>.

Meaning: _____

5. Jennifer fished off the <u>bank</u>.

Meaning: _____

6. Skiers wear a boot on each <u>foot</u>.

Meaning: _____

7. The hot dog was one <u>foot</u> long.

Meaning: _____

8. The woodpecker tapped on the <u>bark</u>.

Meaning: _____

9. Dogs often <u>bark</u> at mail carriers.

Meaning: _____

▶ The /o/ and /aw/ Sounds

Word List

1. fog
2. flop
3. jog
4. off
5. cot
6. spot

Selection Words

7. soft
8. tops
9. drops
10. long

Pattern Study

Look at the pattern:

dog   got

Pronounce each word and listen for the middle sound. These words contain the /o/ or /aw/ sound, both spelled *o*.

▶ Write the spelling words with the /o/ and /aw/ sounds spelled with the same spelling pattern as *dog*.

1. _____ 2. _____ 3. _____

▶ Write the spelling words with the /o/ and /aw/ sounds spelled with the same spelling pattern as *plot*.

4. _____ 5. _____

▶ Which other spelling words have the /o/ and /aw/ sound spelled *o*?

6. _____ 8. _____ 10. _____

7. _____ 9. _____

UNIT 2 Kindness • **Lesson 4** *Butterfly House*

▶ **The /o/ and /aw/ Sounds**

Strategies

 Proofreading Strategy Circle the words that are spelled wrong. Then write the correct spellings in the blanks below.

A flying insect draps down beside you. Can you spat whether it is a moth or a butterfly? Most moths have saft, hairy bodies, while butterflies do not. You can see the tups of a butterfly's wings while it is resting. Dull moths are hard to see in a foog, while butterflies are bright.

11. _____   14. _____

12. _____   15. _____

13. _____

 Meaning Strategy Complete the sentences with the same word used in two different ways. Choose from the words:

      spot   **tops**   **long**

16. Can you _____ the _____ on the horse's head?

17. The toy _____ spun on the _____ of the tables.

18. Do you _____ for a _____ time on the beach?

SPELLING

Name _____ Date _____

 # Homographs

> **Homographs** are words that have the same spelling, but different pronunciations and meanings.
>
> | | | |
> |---|---|---|
> | **object** | disagree | thing |
> | **present** | gift | introduce |
> | **bow** | pretty knot | bend forward |

 **Write the meaning of the underlined word. Then pronounce the word.**

1. What is that strange <u>object</u> on your desk?

Object means: _____.

2. A <u>present</u> from a friend is a nice gift.

Present means: _____.

3. A <u>bow</u> looks nice on a present.

Bow means: _____.

4. <u>Bow</u> after your concert performance.

Bow means: _____.

5. I strongly <u>object</u> to littering.

Object means: _____.

▶**Homographs**

VOCABULARY

Practice

Use the homographs below to complete the sentences. Use each word twice. A dictionary may help.

dove   read   lead   bow   present

6. The metal they used was _____.

7. _____ a good book every day.

8. A manager may _____ an athlete with a trophy.

9. Children _____ for the candy from the piñata.

10. A queen expects her subjects to _____.

11. The _____ runner was the winner.

12. Poodles often have a _____ tied in their fur.

13. Newspapers can be _____ online.

14. Baseball teams have nine players _____ on the field.

15. A symbol of peace is the _____.

Name _____ Date _____

▶ The /u/ Sound

Pattern Study

Look at the patterns:

c<u>u</u>p   f<u>u</u>nd

Pronounce each word and listen for the middle sound. Both words contain the /u/ sound spelled *u*.

Word List

1. us
2. mud
3. rust
4. luck
5. rug
6. duck

Selection Words

7. must
8. hug
9. much
10. shut

▶Write the spelling words with the /u/ sound followed by one consonant as in *gum*.

1. _____   2. _____   3. _____

▶Write the spelling words with the /u/ sound followed by two consonants as in *tuck*.

4. _____   6. _____   8. _____

5. _____   7. _____

▶Write the other spelling words with the /u/ sound spelled *u*.

9. _____   10. _____

UNIT 2 Kindness • **Lesson 5** *Corduroy*

▶ **The /u/ Sound**

Strategies

Visualization Strategy Circle the correct spelling for each word. Then write the word.

11. us   es   _____

12. ducke   duck   _____

13. hug   heg   _____

14. much   moch   _____

15. shuut   shut   _____

Rhyming Strategy Write the spelling word that rhymes with each set of words below. The new word will have the same spelling pattern for /u/. The first one is done for you.

16. cud   bud   mud

17. bug   hug   _____

18. dust   rust   _____

19. tuck   duck   _____

20. dust   must   _____

Exceptions

The /u/ sound can also be spelled *o* as in *son* or **o-consonant-e** as in *glove*, *love*, and *come*.

SPELLING

UNIT 2 Kindness • **Lesson 6** *The Story of Three Whales*

 # Shades of Meaning

> **Shades of Meaning** words have specific definitions that make sentences more meaningful.
>
> You can say, "Whales are big," but if you say, "Whales are enormous," the meaning will be clearer.

 **Match the following words with the words that are similar. Then use them in the sentences.**

tiny   chilly   warm   microscopic   frozen   burning

1. small _____ _____

An insect is _____, but germs are _____.

2. cold _____ _____

We both had cold juice. Mine was just _____. Dave

could hold his upside down, because it was _____.

3. hot _____ _____

We went to the beach on a summer day. The sand was

_____, but the parking lot was _____ hot.

▶**Shades of Meaning**

VOCABULARY

Practice

Fill in the blanks with the Shades of Meaning words below. Use each word one time.

old	strong	quick
shiny	big	cold

The Arctic is an area around the North Pole.

The first trip to the _____ Arctic was

completed in 1909. To reach this area, dog

sleds were once used; now scientists travel by

_____ helicopters. Explorers have

discovered _____ fossils and valuable

minerals there. They have also found ivory

fossils from _____ mammoths.

Animals that live in the Arctic include the polar

bear, _____ musk ox, and reindeer.

At night you may see the _____

northern lights.

Name _____ Date _____

▶ The Final /ən/ Sound

Word List

1. robin
2. dragon
3. chicken
4. lemon
5. wagon
6. cabin

Selection Words

7. broken
8. seven
9. open
10. person

Pattern Study

Look at the patterns:

cous<u>in</u>   elev<u>en</u>   butt<u>on</u>

The final /ən/ sound may be spelled *in, en,* or *on*.

▶ Write the spelling words that have the final /ən/ sound spelled like *button*.

1. _____   3. _____

2. _____   4. _____

▶ Write the spelling words that have the final /ən/ sound spelled like *eleven*.

5. _____   7. _____

6. _____   8. _____

▶ Write the spelling words that have the final /ən/ sound spelled like *cousin*.

9. _____   10. _____

▶ **The Final /ən/ Sound**

Strategies

Visualization Strategy Circle the correct spelling for each word. Then write the word correctly.

11. wagon   waggon   _____

12. sevin   seven   _____

13. brokin   broken   _____

14. cabin   cabbin   _____

15. lemmon   lemon   _____

Proofreading Strategy Circle the words that are spelled incorrectly. Then write the correct words on the lines below.

A roben and a chickin are birds. A dragen is not a bird, but it is not real. A persan who wants to get to know a dragon can opin a book.

16. _____   19. _____

17. _____   20. _____

18. _____

Exceptions

At the end of a word, the final /ən/ sound may be spelled *an*, as in *organ*; or *ain*, as in *curtain*.

SPELLING

Name _____ Date _____

▶Review

> **Homographs** are words that have the same spelling, but different pronunciations and meanings.
>
> | | | |
> |---|---|---|
> | **close** | shut | near |
> | **read** | look at writing | looked at writing |
> | **desert** | hot, dry place | leave |

 **Write the meaning of the underlined word. Then pronounce the word.**

1. Camels cross the Sahara <u>desert</u>.

   Desert means: _____

2. <u>Close</u> the mailbox after you get the letter.

   Close means: _____

3. I like to <u>read</u> comic books.

   Read means: _____

4. I hope my team doesn't <u>desert</u> me today. It is cold.

   Desert means: _____

5. Chinwe moved <u>close</u> to my house.

   Close means: _____

Review • Spelling and Vocabulary Skills

UNIT 2 Kindness • **Lesson 7** *Cinderella*

▶**Review**

Practice

Use these homophones to complete the sentences. A dictionary may help.

ate	sew	foul	red	daze
eight	so	fowl	read	days

6. A baseball that is not hit fair is _____.

7. Mix yellow and _____ to make orange.

8. A spider has _____ legs.

9. I like sunny _____ better than rainy ones.

10. My father likes to _____ his own clothes.

11. A tabby cat _____ the bird.

12. The dictionary can't be _____ in one day.

13. Study hard _____ that you'll get good grades.

14. The animal was lost and in a _____.

15. A turkey is a kind of _____.

VOCABULARY

▶Review

Word List

1. have
2. has
3. west
4. bend
5. milk
6. log

Selection Words

7. got
8. rush
9. rags
10. love

Pattern Study

▶Write the spelling words with the same vowel sound as *sad*.

1. _____   3. _____

2. _____

▶Write the spelling words with the same vowel sound as *pet*.

4. _____   5. _____

▶Write the spelling words with the same vowel sound as *dog* and *cot*.

6. _____   7. _____

▶Write the spelling word with the same vowel sound as *silk*.

8. _____

▶Write the spelling words with the same vowel sound as *much*.

9. _____   10. _____

UNIT 2 Kindness • **Lesson 7** *Cinderella*

▶**Review**

Strategies

 Consonant-Substitution Strategy Replace the underlined letter to create a spelling word. Then write the new word. The first one is done for you.

11. <u>s</u>ilk + *m* = milk

12. <u>f</u>og + *l* = _____

13. <u>b</u>est + *w* = _____

14. ha<u>t</u> + *s* = _____

15. go<u>b</u> + t = _____

 Rhyming Strategy Write the spelling word that rhymes with each set of words below. The new word will have the same spelling pattern and short vowel sound.

16. fend   send   _____

17. sags   bags   _____

18. hot   not   _____

19. mush   hush   _____

20. dog   cog   _____

SPELLING

Name _____ Date _____

▶Base Word Families

A base word is a word that can stand alone. It will give you a clue to the meaning of other words in its family.

Base Word   **Base Word Family Members**
wait   waited, waiter, waiting

 Add the suffixes to the base words below. Write the new words.

1. trail + ing _____

         + er _____

2. stay + ed _____

         + ing _____

3. wait + er _____

         + ed _____

         + ing _____

4. wild + er _____

         + est _____

         + ly _____

►**Base Word Families**

The prefix *over-* means *too much.*
The prefix *re-* means *again.*
The prefix *un-* means *not.*

Add prefixes to the base words below to create new words in the base word family. Then write the meaning of the new word. The first one is done for you.

5. un   +   safe   = unsafe

   Meaning: not safe

6. re   +   sell   = _____

   Meaning: _____

7. un   +   like   = _____

   Meaning: _____

8. un   +   real   = _____

   Meaning: _____

9. re   +   pack   = _____

   Meaning: _____

10. over   +   use   = _____

    Meaning: _____

VOCABULARY

UNIT 3 Look Again • **Lesson I** *I See Animals Hiding*

▶ The /ā/ Sound

Word List

1. trail
2. pail
3. wait
4. cane
5. say
6. fake

Selection Words

7. safe
8. stay
9. way
10. snake

Pattern Study

Look at the patterns:

a_e   ai_   _ay

The /ā/ sound is most frequently spelled with these patterns.

▶ Write the spelling words with the /ā/ sound spelled like *bait*.

1. _____   3. _____

2. _____

▶ Write the spelling words with the /ā/ sound spelled like *away*.

4. _____   6. _____

5. _____

▶ Write the spelling words with the /ā/ sound spelled like *brake*.

7. _____   9. _____

8. _____   10. _____

UNIT 3 Look Again • **Lesson I** *I See Animals Hiding*

▶The /ā/ Sound

SPELLING

Strategies

Rhyming Strategy Write the spelling word that rhymes with each set of words below. The new word should have the same spelling pattern for /ā/. The first one is done for you.

11. pail   snail   trail

12. bait   gait   _____

13. lane   mane   _____

14. day   play   _____

15. rake   fake   _____

Proofreading Strategy Circle the misspelled words. Rewrite the words correctly below.

A sneke may have colorful markings to keep it saaf. One wai to protect itself is by blending with backgrounds of the same color. A gray snake may staye next to a tin pael or a pile of rocks.

16. _____   19. _____

17. _____   20. _____

18. _____

Exceptions

The /ā/ sound may also be spelled *a* as in *able*, *ea* as in *great*, *eigh* as is *weigh*, and *ei* as in *rein*.

▶ Prefixes

> A **prefix** is added to the beginning of a word and changes the meaning of that word.
>
> Prefix (Meaning) + Base Word = New Word
>   (New Meaning)
>
> **un-**   (not, or   +   happy   = unhappy
>   opposite of)   (not happy)
>
> **over-** (too much) + spend   = overspend
>   (spend too much)

 **Add the prefix *un-* to the base words below. Write the new meanings of each new word. The first one is done for you.**

Base Word	New Word	New Meaning
1. lock	unlock	not locked
2. ripe	_____	_____
3. fair	_____	_____

Add the prefix *over-* to the base words below. Write the new meanings of each new word.

Base Word	New Word	New Meaning
4. eat	_____	_____
5. pay	_____	_____

▶**Prefixes**

Practice

**Fill in the blank with the prefix *over-* or *un-*
to create a new word that makes sense in
the sentence. The first one is done for you.**

6. The door is shut, and I need a key to <u>un</u>lock it.

7. An actor may _____act, and make a play awful.

8. Do not _____buckle your seatbelt while the car is
moving.

9. If you do not count your money, you may _____pay.

10. I caught a small fish, so I will _____hook it.

11. Milk will spill if you _____fill your glass.

12. The paper airplane will not fly if you _____fold it.

13. A dragon is an _____real animal.

14. I turn my light off because I am _____afraid of the
dark.

15. That swimming pool will _____flow when people
dive in it.

VOCABULARY

▶ The /ē/ Sound

Word List

1. dream
2. eve
3. silly
4. happy
5. these
6. team

Selection Words

7. feet
8. leaves
9. green
10. sneak

Pattern Study

Look at the patterns:

| ea | _y | ee | e_e |

The /ē/ sound is most frequently spelled with these patterns.

▶ Write the spelling words with the /ē/ sound spelled like *leaf*.

1. _____   3. _____

2. _____   4. _____

▶ Write the spelling words with the /ē/ sound spelled like *funny*.

5. _____   6. _____

▶ Write the spelling words with the /ē/ sound spelled like *seed*.

7. _____   8. _____

▶ Write the spelling words with the /ē/ sound spelled like *scene*.

9. _____   10. _____

UNIT 3 Look Again • **Lesson 2** *They Thought They Saw Him*

▶ **The /ē/ Sound**

Strategies

Visualization Strategy Circle the correct spelling for each word. Then write the word.

11. dream   dreem   _____

12. eav   eve   _____

13. team   teme   _____

14. happie   happy   _____

15. leaves   leves   _____

Pronunciation Strategy Underline the letters that spell the /ē/ sound in each word as you pronounce them. Then, write the spelling word with the same spelling of the /ē/ sound as each set of words below. The first one is done for you.

16. crazy   lazy   silly

17. feed   seen   _____

18. leap   leak   _____

19. scene   eve   _____

20. sleep   reed   _____

Name _____ Date _____

▶ Compound Words

> **Compound words** are formed when two words are put together to make a new word.
>
> dog + house = doghouse
> pan + cake = pancake

 **Combine the words below to form compound words.**

1. shoe + box = _____

2. hat + rack = _____

3. back + ache = _____

4. head + light = _____

5. night + time = _____

6. coat + rack = _____

7. head + ache = _____

8. shoe + shine = _____

9. night + stand = _____

10. hat + box = _____

▶**Compound Words**

VOCABULARY

Practice

Fill in the blanks below with a compound word. The first one is done for you.

11. A house used for a dog is a <u>doghouse</u>.

12. A mark used in books is a _____.

13. A lace used to tie shoes is a _____.

14. A cloth put on a table is a _____.

15. A house used for birds is a _____.

16. A cycle with a motor is a _____.

17. A case to put books in is a _____.

18. A knob for a door is a _____.

19. A box to put mail in is a _____.

20. A yard at a farm is a _____.

▶ The /ī/ Sound

Word List

1. tie
2. cry
3. fly
4. light
5. night
6. pie

Selection Words

7. like
8. hide
9. right
10. find

Pattern Study

Look at the patterns:

i   i_e   _ie   _y   igh

The /ī/ sound is most frequently spelled with these patterns.

▶ Write the spelling words with the /ī/ sound spelled like *try*.

1. _____   2. _____

▶ Write the spelling words with the /ī/ sound spelled like *fight*.

3. _____   5. _____

4. _____

▶ Write the spelling words with the /ī/ sound spelled like *ripe*.

6. _____   7. _____

▶ Write the spelling words with the /ī/ sound spelled like *lie*.

8. _____   9. _____

▶**The /ī/ Sound**

SPELLING

Strategies

Rhyming Strategy Write the word that rhymes with each set of words below. The new word will have the same spelling pattern for /ī/. The first one is done for you.

10. tie   die   pie   **13.** fly   by   _____

11. cry   try   _____   **14.** pie   lie   _____

12. right   light   _____

Proofreading Strategy Circle the misspelled words. Rewrite the words correctly below.

A jackrabbit is a hare. Although they are much alike, hares are different from rabbits. Both hied from predators lyke hawks and coyotes. Hares are usually larger. Rabbits have shorter ears and you can finde them in groups. Ryte at birth hares have fur, while rabbits do not. Most rabbits burrow, away from the bright lite, while hares build nests.

Exceptions
The /ī/ sound may also be spelled *uy* as in *buy* and *guy*.

15. _____   **18.** _____

16. _____   **19.** _____

17. _____

▶Suffixes

> The suffix **-er** may mean *more*.
> The suffix **-est** means *most*.

 **Add suffixes to the base words below to create new words in the base word family. Then write the meaning of each new word. The first one is done for you.**

1. quiet   +   er   =   quieter

Meaning: more quiet

2. kind   +   est   =   _____

Meaning: _____

3. mean   +   est   =   _____

Meaning: _____

4. green   +   er   =   _____

Meaning: _____

5. soft   +   er   =   _____

Meaning: _____

▶ **Suffixes**

Practice

Complete the sentences by adding the suffix -er or -est to the word to make a meaningful sentence. The first one is done for you.

6. I had a small ice cream cone, but Jane's was small<u>er</u>.

7. My dog is soft; my friend's is softer; but this poodle is

   soft_____.

8. Aunt Ida is kind, but my Uncle Jeremy is kind_____.

9. A car is fast, but a plane is fast_____.

10. I don't like green bananas, and that one is green_____ than grass.

11. That lamp is bright, but I need a bright_____ one.

12. The newspaper carrier is loud, but his car is even

    loud_____.

13. A letter is a quick way to communicate, but e-mail is

    quick_____.

14. In the animal kingdom, the cheetah is the fast_____ animal.

15. A turtle is slow, but a snail is slow_____.

VOCABULARY

Name _____ Date _____

► The /ō/ Sound

Word List

1. boat

2. coat

3. poke

4. soap

5. toe

6. blow

7. note

Selection Words

8. show

9. over

10. slowly

Pattern Study

Look at the patterns:

o   _ow   o_e   oa_   _oe

The /ō/ sound is most frequently spelled with these patterns.

► Write the spelling words with the /ō/ sound spelled like *float*.

1. _____   3. _____

2. _____

► Write the spelling words with the /ō/ sound spelled like *vote*.

4. _____   5. _____

► Write the other spelling words with the /ō/ sound.

6. _____   9. _____

7. _____   10. _____

8. _____

▶The /ō/ Sound

Strategies

Consonant-Substitution Strategy Replace the underlined letter or letters to create a spelling word. The new word will have the same spelling for the /ō/ sound.

11. soa<u>k</u>   + *p* = _____

12. <u>g</u>oat   + *b* = _____

13. slow<u>ed</u> + *ly* = _____

14. <u>f</u>low   + *b* = _____

15. <u>t</u>ote   + *n* = _____

Rhyming Strategy Write the spelling word that rhymes with each set of words below. The new word will have the same spelling pattern for the /ō/ sound.

16. boat   float   _____

17. doe   foe   _____

18. blow   snow   _____

19. smoke   choke   _____

> **Exceptions**
> The /ō/ sound may also be spelled *ough* as in *though*.

SPELLING

▶ Suffixes

A **suffix** is added to the end of a word and changes the meaning of the word.
The suffix **-ly** added to a word means "in a _____ way."

 **Add -ly to the following words to create new words that show the way in which something is done.**

1. nice   + ly = _____

2. quiet   + ly = _____

3. deep   + ly = _____

4. brave   + ly = _____

Add -ing to the following words. If a word ends in e, drop the e before adding -ing.

5. show   + ing = _____

6. hope   + ing = _____

7. wait   + ing = _____

8. make   + ing = _____

▶**Suffixes**

Practice

Words ending in *e* drop the *e* before adding
-ing. Combine the base word and suffix to
create new words ending with *-ing*. Then
create a new word with the suffix *-ly*.
The first one is done for you.

9. like + ing = liking

10. like + ly = likely

11. close + ing = _____

12. close + ly = _____

13. love + ing = _____

14. love + ly = _____

Words with a short-vowel sound that end in
a single consonant double the final
consonant before adding *-ing*. Combine the
base words and suffixes to create new words
ending with *-ing*.

15. shop + ing = _____

16. nap + ing = _____

17. let + ing = _____

18. shut + ing = _____

VOCABULARY

▶ The /o͞o/ Sound

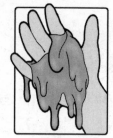

Word List

1. boot
2. food
3. moon
4. room
5. tune
6. rude

Selection Words

7. knew
8. too
9. do
10. who

Pattern Study

Look at the patterns:

oo   u_e   ew   o

The /o͞o/ sound is most frequently spelled with these patterns.

▶ Write the spelling words with the /o͞o/ sound spelled like *root*.

1. _____   4. _____

2. _____   5. _____

3. _____

▶ Write the spelling words with the /o͞o/ sound spelled like *June*.

6. _____   7. _____

▶ Write the spelling words with the /o͞o/ sound spelled like *to*.

8. _____   9. _____

▶ Which word has the /o͞o/ sound spelled like *flew*?

10. _____

UNIT 3 **Look Again • Lesson 5** *How the Guinea Fowl Got Her Spots*

▶ The /o͞o/ Sound

Strategies

Proofreading Strategy Circle the misspelled spelling words. Rewrite the words correctly below.

A young guinea fowl takes about a month to hatch from an egg. These birds were once wild, but now people whoo raise them dou it on farms. Fude these birds eat includes bugs and seeds. Guinea fowl help gardeners by eating rood and pesky bugs. They even eat bees, two!

11. _____   14. _____

12. _____   15. _____

13. _____

Consonant-Substitution Strategy Replace the underlined letter or letters to create a spelling word. The new word will have the same spelling for the /o͞o/ sound.

16. <u>r</u>oot   + *b*   = _____   19. <u>d</u>une + *t*   = _____

17. <u>s</u>oon   + *m* = _____   20. <u>st</u>ew + *kn* = _____

18. <u>gl</u>oom + *r*   = _____

▶Review

A **prefix** is added to the beginning of a word
and changes the meaning of that word.

Prefix (Meaning) + Base Word = New Word
                                               (New Meaning)

un-   (not, or   +   wind   = unwind
           opposite of)   (opposite
                                                  of wind)

over- (too much) + act   = overact
                                               (act too much)

 **Try It!**   **Add the prefix *un-* to the base words below.
Write the new meanings of each new word.**

Base Word   New Word   New Meaning

1. knot   _____   _____

2. even   _____   _____

3. done   _____   _____

**Add the prefix *over-* to the base words below.
Write the new meanings of each new word.**

Base Word   New Word   New Meaning

4. do   _____   _____

5. pay   _____   _____

UNIT 3 **Look Again • Lesson 6** *Animal Camouflage*

▶**Review**

Practice

Complete the sentences by adding the suffix *-er* to the word to make a meaningful sentence.

6. That crayon is light, but I need a light_____one.

7. The stereo is loud, but the radio is even loud_____.

8. A rabbit is quick, but a fox is quick_____.

9. Brown is dark_____ than yellow.

10. Wool is warm_____ than cotton.

11. Insects are small, but bacteria are small_____.

12. My homework is hard, but my older brother's is even

    hard_____.

13. My principal is kind, but my teacher is kind_____.

14. Ice is cold_____ than water.

15. It is warm_____ in spring than in winter.

VOCABULARY

UNIT 3 Look Again • **Lesson 6** *Animal Camouflage*

▶ Review

Word List

1. rake
2. plate
3. might
4. deep
5. meal
6. shy

Selection Words

7. snow
8. seals
9. costume
10. weak

▶ Write the spelling words with the same long-vowel sound as *wait*.

1. _____ 2. _____

▶ Write the spelling words with the same long-vowel sound as *green*.

3. _____ 5. _____

4. _____ 6. _____

▶ Write the spelling words with the same long-vowel sound as *night*.

7. _____ 8. _____

▶ Which spelling word has the same long-vowel sound as *grow*?

9. _____

▶ Which spelling word has the same long-vowel sound as *moon*?

10. _____

►**Review**

Strategies

 Rhyming Strategy Write the spelling word that rhymes with each set of words below. The new word will have the same spelling pattern for the long-vowel sound.

11. late   fate   _____

12. snake   fake   _____

13. sleep   creep   _____

14. low   blow   _____

15. speak   squeak   _____

 Visualization Strategy Circle the correct spelling for each word. Then write the word.

16. myte   might   _____

17. meal   meel   _____

18. shy   shi   _____

19. seals   seels   _____

20. costoom   costume   _____

SPELLING

▶Concept Words

A **concept word** describes how something happens, but does not have a simple one-word definition. You must understand something that is happening to understand the word.

The word **petrified** can mean "something that has changed to stone" or "a stone-like material." We can make a word map of words that help us understand the word *petrified*.

 **Fill in the blanks with the words below to complete the word map.**

plants   fossils   minerals

petrified

What becomes petrified   Names for petrified things

What is needed

	water	
wood		petrified wood
animals	no oxygen	

Concept Words • Spelling and Vocabulary Skills

UNIT 4 Fossils • **Lesson I** *Fossils Tell of Long Ago*

▶**Concept Words**

VOCABULARY

Practice

Complete the word map for the word *preserved* with the words below.

mammoth   snow   amber

The story "Fossils Tell of Long Ago" will help.

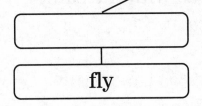

preserved

What becomes preserved

fly

What helps preserve it

Use a dictionary to help you understand words you do not know.

Complete the word map for the word *fossils* with the words below.

extinct   tracks   fish   age

fossils

What becomes a fossil

plants

What they teach us about

creatures

Earth

Spelling and Vocabulary Skills • *Concept Words*

UNIT 4 Fossils • **Lesson 1** *Fossils Tell of Long Ago*

► Words with *wh* and *sh*

Word List

1. clash
2. flash
3. shine
4. shore
5. why
6. where

Selection Words

7. while
8. what
9. when
10. fresh

Pattern Study

Look at the patterns:

why   shy

These letters combine to form one sound.

► Write the spelling words with the same beginning sound as *share.*

1. _____   2. _____

► Write the spelling words with the same ending sound as *wish.*

3. _____   5. _____

4. _____

► Write the spelling words with the same beginning sound as *which.*

6. _____   9. _____

7. _____   10. _____

8. _____

UNIT 4 Fossils • **Lesson 1** *Fossils Tell of Long Ago*

▶**Words with *wh* and *sh***

Strategies

Visualization Strategy Circle the correct spelling for each word. Then write the word.

11. clach   clash   _____

12. flasche   flash   _____

13. shore   shor   _____

14. shien   shine   _____

15. where   weare   _____

Proofreading Strategy Circle the words that are spelled incorrectly. Then write the correct words on the lines below.

Wy is a fossil formed? A fossil is wat forms when a plant or animal is covered in something that does not let it rot. A frech leaf may become a fossil wile it is covered in mud. Wen it is left that way for many years, the mud may form a type of rock with a fossil.

16. _____   19. _____

17. _____   20. _____

18. _____

SPELLING

▶Synonyms

Synonyms are words with similar meanings.

 Replace the word *town* in the sentences below to create more meaningful sentences. A dictionary may help.

Fill in the blanks with one of the following synonyms for *town*: suburb village

1. It is hard to find a hotel in this tiny little <u>town</u>.

It is hard to find a hotel in this tiny little _____.

2. This <u>town</u> is a small area just outside of Tampa.

This _____ is a small area just outside of Tampa.

Fill in the blanks with one of these synonyms for *city*: metropolis capital city

3. Mayors meet in this <u>city</u>.

Mayors meet in this _____.

4. You can easily find a taxi in a big <u>city</u>.

You can easily find a taxi in a big _____.

Synonyms • Spelling and Vocabulary Skills

UNIT 4 Fossils • **Lesson 2** *The Dinosaur Who Lived in My Backyard*

▶**Synonyms**

Practice

Replace the word *shake* in the sentences below to create more meaningful sentences. A dictionary may help.

Fill in the blanks with one of the following synonyms:

wriggle   tremble   squirm   vibrate   jolt

5. The train suddenly stopped, and gave us a <u>shake</u>.

The train suddenly stopped, and gave us a _____.

6. The baby began to <u>shake</u> in its mother's arms.

The baby began to _____ in its mother's arms.

7. During an earthquake, the ground may <u>shake</u>.

During an earthquake, the ground may _____.

8. A small child may <u>shake</u> during a long speech.

A small child may _____ during a long speech.

9. That house will <u>shake</u> when a train rolls by.

That house will _____ when a train rolls by.

VOCABULARY

UNIT 4 Fossils • **Lesson 2** *The Dinosaur Who Lived in My Backyard*

▶ Words with *ch* and *th*

Word List

1. chick

2. choke

3. thick

4. peach

5. teach

6. thin

Selection Words

7. there

8. they

9. hatched

10. mother

Pattern Study

Look at the patterns:

<u>ch</u>in   <u>th</u>in

These letters combine to make one sound.

▶ Write the spelling words with the same beginning spelling pattern as *cheat*.

1. _____   2. _____

▶ Write the spelling words with the same beginning spelling pattern as *those*.

3. _____   5. _____

4. _____   6. _____

▶ Write the spelling words ending like *which*.

7. _____   8. _____

▶ Write a spelling word that rhymes with each word.

9. *matched* _____

10. *other* _____

Words with ch and th • Spelling and Vocabulary Skills

▶ **Words with *ch* and *th***

Strategies

 Vowel-Substitution Strategy Replace the underlined vowel sounds to create a spelling word.

11. ch<u>e</u>ck   + i   = _____

12. th<u>a</u>n   + i   = _____

13. p<u>oa</u>ch   + ea   = _____

14. h<u>i</u>tched   + a   = _____

 Rhyming Strategy Write the spelling word that rhymes with each word below. The first one is done for you.

15. broke   choke

16. sick   _____

17. reach   _____

18. where   _____

19. hey   _____

20. brother   _____

▶Science Words

> **Science Words** help us explore and understand the world around us. **Scientists** are people who study many different things.

 Fill in the blank with one thing that these scientists are curious about. Looking at parts of the word or using a dictionary may help. The first one is done for you.
Choose from:

chemicals animals math fossils books

1. A paleontologist is curious about <u>fossils</u>.

2. A veterinarian is curious about _____.

3. A librarian is curious about _____.

4. A chemist is curious about _____.

5. A mathematician studies _____.

**There are many types of scientists.
Scientists can study anything in the world
that they are curious about.**

▶**Science Words**

Practice

-ologist means "someone who studies."

Use the hints provided to learn what these scientists study.

6. *geo* means "earth"

A *geologist* studies the _____.

7. *bio* means "life"

A *biologist* studies _____.

8. *zo* means "animal"

A *zoologist* studies _____.

9. *ichthys* means "fish"

An *ichthyologist* studies _____.

10. *eco* means "surroundings"

An *ecologist* studies our _____.

VOCABULARY

UNIT 4 Fossils • **Lesson 3** *Dinosaur Fossils*

▶ The /ar/ Sound

Word List
1. cart
2. sharp
3. farm
4. smart
5. shark
6. arm

Selection Words
7. yard
8. part
9. are
10. harden

Pattern Study

Look at the pattern:

<u>car</u>   st<u>ar</u>t

The /ar/ sound can be spelled *ar*.

▶ Write the spelling words with the same beginning sound as *art*.

1. _____   2. _____

▶ Write the spelling words that rhyme with *start*.

3. _____   5. _____

4. _____

▶ Write the other spelling words with the /ar/ sound.

6. _____   9. _____

7. _____   10. _____

8. _____

UNIT 4 Fossils • **Lesson 3** *Dinosaur Fossils*

▶**The /ar/ Sound**

SPELLING

Strategies

 Consonant-Substitution Strategy Replace the underlined letter in each word with a new letter to form a spelling word. The first one is done for you.

11. yar<u>n</u> + d = yard

12. ar<u>k</u> + m = _____

13. ar<u>t</u> + e = _____

14. car<u>d</u> + t = _____

15. par<u>k</u> + t = _____

 Visualization Strategy Circle the spelling words that are spelled correctly. Then write the correct word on the line.

16. farm   ferm   _____

17. smirt   smart   _____

18. sharp   shrp   _____

19. sharc   shark   _____

20. harden   hardn   _____

Name _____ Date _____

▶Antonyms

> **Antonyms** are words that are opposite or
> nearly opposite in meaning.
> *Good* and *bad* are antonyms.

Try It! **Match the following words with their antonyms. The first one is done for you.**

1. lock   unhappy

2. before   under

3. over   mean

4. happy   after

5. nice   unlock

Now try these:

6. fix   outside

7. sad   happy

8. above   unwind

9. inside   break

10. wind   below

UNIT 4 Fossils • **Lesson 4** *Why Did the Dinosaurs Disappear?*

▶**Antonyms**

Practice

Complete the sentences with an antonym.

11. The opposite of last is _____.

12. The opposite of girl is _____.

13. The opposite of short is _____.

14. Another opposite of short is _____.

15. The opposite of more is _____.

Add the prefix to create an antonym. The first one is done for you.

16. dis + obey = disobey

17. un + pack = _____

18. un + known = _____

19. dis + honor = _____

20. un + cover = _____

VOCABULARY

▶ The /er/ and /or/ Sounds

Word List

1. girl
2. first
3. herd
4. turn
5. short
6. hurt

Selection Words

7. dinosaur
8. for
9. more
10. swirl

Pattern Study

Look at the patterns:

snore   shirt   burn   perch

The /or/ sound is most often spelled *or*.
The /er/ sound is most often spelled *ir, ur,* or *er*.

▶ Write the spelling words with the same vowel sound as *snore*.

1. _____   3. _____

2. _____   4. _____

▶ Write the spelling words with the same vowel sound and vowel spelling as *shirt*.

5. _____   7. _____

6. _____

▶ Write the words with /er/ spelled *ur* and *er*.

8. _____   10. _____

9. _____

UNIT 4 Fossils • **Lesson 4** *Why Did the Dinosaurs Disappear?*

▶**The /er/ and /or/ Sounds**

Strategies

 Proofreading Strategy Circle the words that are spelled incorrectly. Then write the correct words on the lines below.

A hird of sheep needed mour food. The ferst sheep made a tirn onto the road fer home.

11. _____

12. _____

13. _____

14. _____

15. _____

 Visualization Strategy Circle the correct spelling for each word. Then write the word.

16. gril   girl   _____

17. hert   hurt   _____

18. short   shortt   _____

19. dinosaur dinasor   _____

20. swerl   swirl   _____

Exceptions

/or/ may be spelled *oor* as in *door*, or *our* as in *pour*. /er/ may be spelled *ear* as in *heard*.

SPELLING

Name _____ Date _____

▶Analogies

An **analogy** shows a way that two things or ideas are related. An analogy for the words *shallow* and *deep* shows position.
Shallow is to *deep* as *up* is to *down*.

 **Complete these analogies about places and sizes.**

1. Up is to down as

   high is to _____.

2. Over is to under as

   above is to _____.

3. Inside is to outside as

   inner is to _____.

4. Shorter is to taller as

   smaller is to _____.

5. Front is to back as

   light is to _____.

UNIT 4 Fossils • **Lesson 5** *Monster Tracks*

▶**Analogies**

Practice

Complete the analogies below.

Analogies may show how things are similar . . .

6. Jacket is to zipper as shoe is to _____.

7. Whale is to ocean as monkey is to _____.

8. Cup is to juice as plate is to _____.

9. Airplane is to air as boat is to _____.

10. Shoe is to foot as glove is to _____.

. . . or different.

11. Good is to bad as right is to _____.

12. Quiet is to loud as whisper is to _____.

13. East is to west as north is to _____.

14. Cold is to hot as wet is to _____.

15. Right is to left as up is to _____.

VOCABULARY

UNIT 4 Fossils • **Lesson 5** *Monster Tracks*

▶ Words with *br* and *fr*

Word List
1. brag
2. bread
3. brick
4. free
5. frog
6. friend

Selection Words
7. brush
8. bright
9. front
10. frisky

Pattern Study

Look at the patterns:

<u>br</u>own   <u>fr</u>own

These letters combine to make one sound.

▶Write the spelling words with the same beginning sound as *brain*.

1. _____

2. _____

3. _____

4. _____

5. _____

▶Write the spelling words with the same beginning sound as *fright*.

6. _____   9. _____

7. _____   10. _____

8. _____

UNIT 4 Fossils • **Lesson 5** *Monster Tracks*

▶**Words with *br* and *fr***

Strategies

 Pronunciation Strategy Circle the correct spelling for each word. Then pronounce each word as you write it correctly.

11. bread   brid   _____

12. breck   brick   _____

13. frug   frog   _____

14. front   frunt   _____

15. frisky   friskey   _____

16. friend   freind   _____

 Vowel-Substitution Strategy Replace the underlined letter with a new vowel sound to create a spelling word.

17. br<u>i</u>g   + *a*   = _____

18. br<u>a</u>sh   + *u*   = _____

19. fr<u>y</u>   + *ee*   = _____

20. br<u>a</u>t   + *igh* = _____

SPELLING

▶Review

 **Replace the word *cry* in the sentences below to create more meaningful sentences. A dictionary may help.**

Fill in the blanks with one of the following synonyms:

yell   whine   whimper   scream   weep

1. A child may <u>cry</u> for a candy bar.

A child may _____ for a candy bar.

2. Football fans <u>cry</u> out when their team scores.

Football fans _____ out when their team scores.

3. The baby began to <u>cry</u> until Grandpa held her.

The baby began to _____ until Grandpa held her.

4. Some people <u>cry</u> when they are happy.

Some people _____ when they are happy.

5. When I hurt myself, I <u>cry</u> for my parent.

When I hurt myself, I _____ for my parent.

UNIT 4 **Fossils • Lesson 6** *Let's Go Dinosaur Tracking*

▶**Review**

VOCABULARY

Practice

Replace the word *whispered* in the sentences below to create sentences with opposite meanings. A dictionary may help.

Fill in the blanks with one of the following antonyms for *whispered:*

yelled   screamed   hollered   wailed   bellowed

6. The umpire <u>whispered</u>, "You're out!" to the batter.

The umpire _____, "You're out!" to the batter.

7. The librarian <u>whispered</u>, "Eek!" when she saw the spider.

The librarian _____, "Eek!" when she saw the spider.

8. My baby brother <u>whispered</u>, "Waaah!"

My baby brother _____, "Waaah!"

9. The teacher <u>whispered</u>, "Time Out!" to the kindergarten class.

The teacher _____, "Time Out!" to the kindergarten class.

10. The huge cartoon mouse <u>whispered</u> in the cat's ear.

The huge cartoon mouse _____ in the cat's ear.

UNIT 4 Fossils • **Lesson 6** *Let's Go Dinosaur Tracking*

▶Review

Word List

1. shock
2. white
3. third
✓ 4. reach
5. fifth
6. bring

Selection Words

7. formed
8. ever
9. chase
10. fish

▶Write the spelling words with *wh* and *sh*.

1. _____   3. _____

2. _____

▶Write the spelling words with *ch* and *th*.

4. _____   6. _____

5. _____   7. _____

▶Write the spelling words that rhyme with *bird* and *stormed*.

8. _____   9. _____

▶Which spelling word begins with the same sound as *bright?*

10. _____

UNIT 4 Fossils • **Lesson 6** *Let's Go Dinosaur Tracking*

SPELLING

Strategies

 Rhyming Strategy Write the spelling word that rhymes with each word. The new word will have the same spelling pattern for the vowel sound. The first one is done for you.

11. stormed formed

12. bird _____

13. never _____

14. sock _____

 Visualization Strategy Circle the correct spelling for each word. Then write the word.

15. white wite _____

16. rech reach _____

17. bring breg _____

18. chas chase _____

19. fish fesh _____

20. fyfth fifth _____

Name _____ Date _____

Synonyms

> **Synonyms** are words that have the same, or nearly the same meanings.
> *Cold, freezing,* and *icy* are synonyms.

 **Complete the sentences below with a synonym for the given word. The first one is done for you.**

1. plenty   The candy store has <u>lots</u> of chocolate.

2. furious   A _____ bee started flying toward me.

3. large   Jumbo was the _____ elephant at the circus.

4. small   The _____ mouse had cheese in his paws.

5. good   I had a _____ grade in math this time.

6. bad   That _____ dog barks all of the time.

7. joyful   Songs that are _____ are wonderful to hear.

8. ill   I missed school because I was _____.

9. mean   I read a book about a _____ bully.

10. friendly   The doctor was _____ to his patients.

UNIT 5 Courage • **Lesson I** *Molly the Brave and Me*

▶**Synonyms**

{ **Practice** }

Complete the sentences below with a synonym for the given word.

11. gross   Some people think worms are _____.

12. tiny   A germ is _____.

13. huge   The skyscraper was a _____ building.

14. shout   I began to _____ when he hit a home run.

15. laugh   It is hard not to _____ at a pun.

16. cry   Sometimes I _____ when I'm hurt.

17. ruby   A cardinal is a _____ bird.

18. tan   I have a _____ coat with yellow buttons.

19. leaped   The acrobat _____ high into the air.

20. violet   I love flowers that are _____, like lilacs.

VOCABULARY

Name _____ Date _____

▶ Words Ending in *-ed* and *-ing*

Word List

1. cutting
2. batting
3. hitting
4. skipping
5. running
6. mopped

Selection Words

7. swatted
8. slipped
9. spotted
10. kissed

Pattern Study

Look at the patterns:

cut	cutting
mop	mopped

▶ Write the spelling words with the same ending as *fitting*.

1. _____   4. _____

2. _____   5. _____

3. _____

▶ Write the spelling words with the same ending as *fitted*.

6. _____   9. _____

7. _____   10. _____

8. _____

UNIT 5 Courage • **Lesson I** *Molly the Brave and Me*

▶**Words Ending in *-ed* and *-ing***

Strategies

Conventions Strategy Add the *-ed* or *-ing* ending to each word to create a spelling word. Remember to double the final consonant if necessary.

11. swat + ed _____

12. spot + ed _____

13. hit + ing _____

14. cut + ing _____

15. kiss + ed _____

16. skip + ing _____

17. run + ing _____

Vowel-Substitution Strategy Replace the underlined vowel with the new vowel to create a spelling word.

18. m<u>a</u>pped + o _____

19. b<u>e</u>tting + a _____

20. sl<u>a</u>pped + i _____

SPELLING

UNIT 5 Courage • **Lesson 2** *Dragons and Giants*

▶Antonyms

> **Antonyms** are words that are opposite or nearly opposite in meaning. *Right* and *left* are antonyms.

Try It! Write the word from the box that is an antonym.

front	up	narrow	worst	below

1. above _____   4. best _____

2. down _____   5. wide _____

3. back _____

Now try these:

apart	untie	sell	found	empty

6. full _____   9. together _____

7. lost _____   10. buy _____

8. tie _____

UNIT 5 Courage • **Lesson 2** *Dragons and Giants*

▶**Antonyms**

Practice

Complete the sentences with an antonym.

11. The opposite of worst is _____.

12. The opposite of woman is _____.

13. The opposite of tall is _____.

14. The opposite of young is _____.

15. The opposite of enemy is _____.

Add the prefix to create an antonym.
The first one is done for you.

16. dis + respect = disrespect

17. un + happy = _____

18. un + able = _____

19. dis + believe = _____

20. un + bent = _____

VOCABULARY

UNIT 5 Courage • **Lesson 2** *Dragons and Giants*

▶ Present Tense of Words

Word List
1. give
2. drive
3. sing
4. come
5. slide
6. get

Selection Words
7. know
8. fight
9. look
10. tell

Pattern Study

▶Write the spelling word that fits the rhyming pattern.

1. sold   sell

told   _____

2. booked book

looked _____

3. hid   hide

slid   _____

4. rang ring

sang   _____

5. dove dive

drove _____

6. grew grow

knew _____

▶Complete each sentence with a spelling word.

7. Yesterday they fought. Today they

_____.

8. Yesterday I gave. Today I _____.

9. Yesterday I came. Today I _____.

10. Yesterday I got it. Today I _____ it.

UNIT 5 Courage • **Lesson 2** *Dragons and Giants*

▶**Present Tense of Words**

Strategies

Meaning Strategy Write a spelling word to replace the underlined word.

11. I will <u>sang</u> loudly at choir practice. _____

12. Don't <u>slid</u> down the slide after it rains. _____

13. These animals will <u>fought</u> for a banana. _____

14. Make sure to <u>looked</u> for cars before crossing the

street. _____

15. If it starts raining, please <u>came</u> indoors. _____

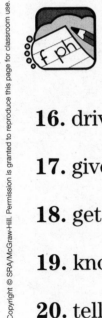

Visualization Strategy Circle the words that are spelled correctly. Then write the correct words.

16. driv   drive   _____

17. give   giv   _____

18. get   git   _____

19. kno   know   _____

20. tell   tel   _____

SPELLING

UNIT 5 Courage • **Lesson 3** *A Hole in the Dike*

▶Base Word Families

A **base word** is a word that can stand alone.
It will give you a clue to the meaning of other
words in its family.

Base Word	**Family Members**
near	nearly
	nears

 **Write the base word for each group
below. The first one is done for you.**

1. heard, hearing, hears   hear

2. skylight, skyscraper, skies _____

3. going, gone, goes _____

4. walk, walking, spacewalk _____

✓ 5. thanked, thanking, thanks _____

6. wanting, wants, wanted _____

7. drinks, drinking, drinker _____

8. starfish, stars, starlight _____

9. dimly, dimmer, dimmest _____

10. sadden, sadder, sadness _____

UNIT 5 Courage • **Lesson 3** *A Hole in the Dike*

▶**Base Word Families**

Practice

Circle the words in the same base word family. Then write the base word and the meaning the words in this family share.

11. slide   slid   sided

Base Word: _____

Meaning: _____

12. locked   looked   looking

Base Word: _____

Meaning: _____

13. driven   drives   diver

Base Word: _____

Meaning: _____

14. every   ever   everyone

Base Word: _____

Meaning: _____

VOCABULARY

UNIT 5 Courage • **Lesson 3** *A Hole in the Dike*

▶ Past Tense of Words

Word List

1. gave
2. came
3. sang
4. drove
5. told
6. was

Selection Words

7. were
8. lived
9. looked
10. slid

Pattern Study

▶Write the spelling word that fits the pattern.

1. sell   sold

tell _____

2. hook hooked

look _____

3. hide   hid

slide _____

4. ring   rang

sing _____

5. dive   dove

drive _____

▶Complete each sentence with a spelling word. The first one is done for you.

6. I will give today. Last week I <u>gave</u>.

7. I will come today. Last week I _____.

8. I am late today. Last week I _____ late.

9. We are happy. Last week we _____ happy.

10. I live in Rome. Last year I _____ in Paris.

UNIT 5 Courage • **Lesson 3** *A Hole in the Dike*

▶**Past Tense of Words**

Strategies

Visualization Strategy Circle the correct spelling of each word. Then write the word.

11. were   wer   _____

12. toled   told   _____

13. drove   drov   _____

14. slid   slyd   _____

15. livd   lived   _____

Meaning Strategy Replace the underlined word with the correct spelling word.

16. I <u>give</u> _____ my dog a bath yesterday.

17. Last week, there <u>is</u> _____ nowhere to play.

18. On Tuesday, I <u>sing</u> _____ the song twice for my aunt.

19. We <u>look</u> _____ everywhere for that shoe yesterday.

20. When it snowed, our cat <u>come</u> _____ inside.

SPELLING

UNIT 5 Courage • **Lesson 4** *Martin Luther King, Jr.*

▶Prefixes

 A prefix is added to the beginning of a word and changes the meaning of that word.

re- (again) + read = reread (read again)
pre- (before) + test = pretest (test before)

Add the prefix *re-* to the base words below. Then write the new meaning of the new word. The first one is done for you.

Base Word	New Word	New Meaning
1. read	reread	read again
2. fill	_____	_____
3. do	_____	_____

Add the prefix *pre-* to the base words below. Then write the meaning of the new word.

Base Word	New Word	New Meaning
4. pay	_____	_____
5. wash	_____	_____
6. dawn	_____	_____

UNIT 5 Courage • **Lesson 4** *Martin Luther King, Jr.*

▶ **Prefixes**

Practice

Add the prefix *pre-* or *re-* to create a new word that makes sense in the sentence. Then write the word. The first one is done for you.

7. We missed the <u>pregame</u> show because we arrived late. <u>pregame</u>

8. I had to _____ take my spelling test again because I did badly the first time.

   _____

9. We watched a _____ view of the movie before we went to see it. _____

10. The color was not right, so the artist had to _____ paint the picture. _____

11. The students were too young for kindergarten, so they went to _____ school.

    _____

12. Please _____ write this sentence again. I can't read it! _____

VOCABULARY

Plurals

Word List

1. glasses
2. washes
3. cows
4. cakes
5. ducks
6. zebras

Selection Words

7. buses
8. marches
9. years
10. stores

Pattern Study

Look at the patterns:

dog   dogs   wish   wishes

-s and *-es* are often added to a word to show that there are more than one.

▶Add *-es* to form the plurals of the words. Then write the whole word.

1. glass   _____   _____

2. wash   _____   _____

3. bus   _____   _____

4. march   _____   _____

▶Add *-s* to form the plurals of the words. Then write the whole word.

5. cow   _____   _____

6. cake   _____   _____

7. duck   _____   _____

8. store   _____   _____

UNIT 5 Courage • **Lesson 4** *Martin Luther King, Jr.*

▶ **Plurals**

Strategies

Rhyming Strategy Write the spelling word that rhymes with each word below. The new word should have the same plural spelling.

9. plows _____

10. bakes _____

11. trucks _____

12. tears _____

13. scores _____

Conventions Strategy Add *-es* or *-s* to the words below to form spelling words. Then write the words.

14. march _____   _____

15. bus _____   _____

16. wash _____   _____

17. glass _____   _____

18. zebra _____   _____

SPELLING

▶Suffixes

> The suffix *-er* may mean "more."
> The suffix *-est* may mean "most."

Try It! Add suffixes to the base words below to create new words in the base word family. Remember that a *y* at the end of a word changes to *i* before the suffix is added. The first one is done for you.

1. silly + er = sillier

2. silly + est = _____

3. happy + er = _____

4. happy + est = _____

5. crazy + er = _____

6. crazy + est = _____

7. angry + er = _____

8. angry + est = _____

9. tiny + er = _____

10. tiny + est = _____

UNIT 5 Courage • **Lesson 5** *The Empty Pot*

▶**Suffixes**

Practice

Add suffixes to the base words below to create words used to compare. The first one is done for you.

11. big   + er   = bigger

12. big   + est   = _____

13. red   + er   = _____

14. red   + est   = _____

15. hot   + er   = _____

16. hot   + est   = _____

Words ending with a double consonant do not add another consonant. Add suffixes to the base words below. The first one is done for you.

17. tall   + er   = taller

18. tall   + est   = _____

19. small   + er   = _____

20. small   + est   = _____

VOCABULARY

▶ Suffixes

Word List

1. higher
2. highest
3. slower
4. slowest
5. happier
6. sillier
7. bigger
8. silliest

Selection Words

9. biggest
10. happiest

Pattern Study

Look at the patterns:

soft	softest
red	reddest
silly	silliest

▶Add *-er* and *-est* to each base word.

slow   1. _____

        2. _____

big   3. _____

        4. _____

silly   5. _____

        6. _____

high   7. _____

        8. _____

happy   9. _____

       10. _____

▶**Suffixes**

SPELLING

Strategies

Proofreading Strategy Circle the words that are spelled incorrectly. Then write the correct words.

New roller coasters are highher than ever before. They are biger and faster than older, slowwer coasters. I would be hapier riding a roller coaster than a merry-go-round, but I would be hapiest riding a tall and exciting one.

11. _____   14. _____

12. _____   15. _____

13. _____

Conventions Strategy Add *-er* or *-est* to the words below to form spelling words.

16. silly + est _____

17. silly + er _____

18. slow + est _____

19. big + est _____

20. high + est _____

►Review

A **prefix** is added to the beginning of a word and changes the meaning of that word.
re- (again) + told = retold (told again)

 **Try It!** Add the prefix *re-* to the base words below. Then write the meaning of the new word. The first one is done for you.

Base Word	New Word	New Meaning
1. fill	refill	fill again
2. mix	_____	_____
3. train	_____	_____
4. start	_____	_____
5. play	_____	_____
6. told	_____	_____
7. enter	_____	_____
8. do	_____	_____
9. copy	_____	_____
10. write	_____	_____

UNIT 5 Courage • **Lesson 6** *Brave as a Mountain Lion*

▶**Review**

VOCABULARY

Practice

**Add suffixes to the base words below.
Write the new word and its meaning.
The first one is done for you.**

11. brave + er = braver
Meaning: more brave

12. brave + est = _____

Meaning: _____

13. safe + er = _____

Meaning: _____

14. safe + est = _____

Meaning: _____

15. blue + er = _____

Meaning: _____

16. easy + er = _____

Meaning: _____

17. nosy + est = _____

Meaning: _____

UNIT 5 Courage • **Lesson 6** *Brave as a Mountain Lion*

▶Review

Word List

1. aunts
2. tapped
3. met
4. whales
5. animals
6. rabbits

Selection Words

7. packed
8. uncles
9. dropping
10. bravest

Pattern Study

▶Write the spelling words that are past-tense words.

1. _____   3. _____

2. _____

▶Write the spelling words that are more than one, or plurals.

4. _____   7. _____

5. _____   8. _____

6. _____

▶Which spelling word means *most brave?*

9. _____

▶Which spelling word was formed by adding *-ing?*

10. _____

UNIT 5 Courage • **Lesson 6** *Brave as a Mountain Lion*

▶**Review**

Strategies

Visualization Strategy Circle the correct spelling for each word. Then write the word.

11. unclees   uncles   _____

12. rabbits   rabbites   _____

13. aunts   auntts   _____

14. meeted   met   _____

15. animalls   animals   _____

16. bravest   bravst   _____

Rhyming Strategy Write the spelling word that rhymes with each word below.

17. trapped   _____

18. whacked   _____

19. stopping   _____

20. tales   _____

SPELLING

Name _____ Date _____

▶ Social Studies Words

 **Try It!** Read the sentences below about the lives of the first Americans. Fill in the blanks with the word below that best fits each sentence.

teepees	hunted	gathered	tools	music

1. The first Americans did not have radios. They made their

   own _____ with drums and whistles.

2. We go to the store to buy _____. Some people long ago made them from bones.

3. Now it is a treat to pick berries. Many years ago, children

   _____ them to survive.

4. People from the plains _____ buffalo to use for food, clothing, and tools.

5. They also used buffalo hide for their homes. These homes

   were called _____.

UNIT 6 Our Country and Its People • **Lesson I** *The First Americans*

▶**Social Studies Words**

Practice

Read the sentences below about the lives of the first Americans. Fill in the blanks with the word below that best fits each sentence.

wrestled	carved	festivals	whaleblubber	dances

6. The first Americans _____ each other for sport.

7. Men and boys also _____ totem poles and decorations.

8. Before electricity, _____ was one thing people burned for light.

9. One thing we do that the first Americans did is to hold _____ to music.

10. The first Americans also held _____ for many reasons.

VOCABULARY

▶ Prefixes

Word List

1. redo
2. retake
3. rename
4. retry
5. retest
6. uneven
7. unpack
8. unlock
9. unroll
10. unsure

Pattern Study

Look at the patterns:

      unnamed   **re**send

The prefixes **un-** and **re-** are added to base words to form new words.

The prefix **un-** may mean "not" and the prefix **re-** may mean "again."

▶ Write the spelling words with the same prefix as **replay**.

1. _____   4. _____

2. _____   5. _____

3. _____

▶ Write the spelling words with the same prefix as **undo**.

6. _____   9. _____

7. _____   10. _____

8. _____

UNIT 6 Our Country and Its People • **Lesson 1** *The First Americans*

▶**Prefixes**

Strategies

 Visualization Strategy Circle the base word. Then rewrite the spelling word.

11. retest _____

12. retry _____

13. rename _____

14. retake _____

15. redo _____

16. unsure _____

17. unroll _____

18. unlock _____

19. unpack _____

20. uneven _____

SPELLING

▶Suffixes

The suffix *-ful* may mean "full of" or "having."
The suffix *-less* may mean "without."

Try It! **Add the suffixes to the base words below to create new words in the base word family. The first one is done for you.**

1. thought + less = thoughtless

2. care + ful = _____

3. care + less = _____

4. use + ful = _____

5. end + less = _____

6. mouth + ful = _____

7. spot + less = _____

8. wish + ful = _____

9. forget + ful = _____

10. help + ful = _____

UNIT 6 **Our Country and Its People • Lesson 2** *New Hope*

▶ **Suffixes**

Practice

Add suffixes to the base words below to create words used to describe. Then write the meaning of the new word.

11. cloud + less = _____

Meaning: _____

12. hair + less = _____

Meaning: _____

13. fear + ful = _____

Meaning: _____

14. bottom + less = _____

Meaning: _____

15. color + ful = _____

Meaning: _____

VOCABULARY

UNIT 6 Our Country and Its People • **Lesson 2** *New Hope*

 # Suffixes

Word List

1. useless
2. clueless
3. jobless
4. shapeless
5. helpless
6. playful
7. hopeful
8. harmful
9. shameful
10. wonderful

Pattern Study

Look at the patterns:

care**ful**   care**less**

The suffixes *-ful* and *-less* may be added to the ends of base words.

▶ Write the spelling words with the same ending as *careless*.

1. _____   4. _____

2. _____   5. _____

3. _____

▶ Write the spelling words with the same ending as *colorful*.

6. _____   9. _____

7. _____   10. _____

8. _____

UNIT 6 Our Country and Its People • **Lesson 2** *New Hope*

▶**Suffixes**

SPELLING

Strategies

 Conventions Strategy Add the suffix *-ful* or *-less* to each word to create a spelling word.

11. help + less = _____

12. use + less = _____

13. wonder + ful = _____

14. hope + ful = _____

15. job + less = _____

 Visualization Strategy Circle the correctly spelled spelling word. Then write the spelling word.

16. cluless   clueless   _____

17. shamful   shameful   _____

18. shapeless   shaepless   _____

19. playful   playfull   _____

20. harmfull   harmful   _____

Name _____ Date _____

▶Compound Words

Compound words are formed when two base words are put together to make a new word.

sun + set = sunset

light + house = lighthouse

Try It! Combine the words below to form compound words.

1. out + side = _____

2. play + room = _____

3. her + self = _____

4. any + body = _____

5. any + one = _____

6. coat + room = _____

7. moon + light = _____

8. base + ball = _____

9. fire + place = _____

10. fire + fly = _____

UNIT 6 Our Country and Its People • **Lesson 3** *A Place Called Freedom*

▶**Compound Words**

Practice

**Fill in the blanks below with a compound word.
The first one is done for you.**

11. A bath for birds is a <u>birdbath</u>.

12. A pen for a pig is a _____.

13. The light from the sun is _____.

14. The shell of an egg is an _____.

15. A shelf for books is a _____.

16. A house for a hen is a _____.

17. A store with books is a _____.

18. A bird that is blue is a _____.

19. A light used at night is a _____.

20. A yard by a barn is a _____.

VOCABULARY

Name _____ Date _____

▶ Compound Words

Word List

1. maybe
2. inside
3. bedroom
4. lunchroom
5. myself
6. nobody

Selection Words

7. sunrise
8. himself
9. railroad
10. everyone

Pattern Study

▶Write the spelling words with the base word *room*.

1. _____

2. _____

▶Write the spelling words with the base word *self*.

3. _____

4. _____

▶Put the words below together to make spelling words.

5. may   +   be   _____

6. in   +   side   _____

7. no   +   body   _____

8. sun   +   rise   _____

9. rail   +   road   _____

10. every +   one   _____

UNIT 6 Our Country and Its People • **Lesson 3** *A Place Called Freedom*

▶**Compound Words**

SPELLING

Strategies

 Compound Word Strategy Combine the base words below to form spelling words.

11. lunch + room = _____

12. him + self = _____

13. bed + room = _____

14. in + side = _____

15. my + self = _____

 Conventions Strategy Match the words to form a spelling word. Then write the spelling word on the line below. The first one is done for you.

16. may   body

maybe

17. no   be

_____

18. sun   rise

_____

►Homophones

A **homophone** is a word that has the same sound as another word, but it has a different spelling and meaning.

 **Complete the sentence using** *fourth* **or** *forth*. **Then write the meaning of the homophone.**

Fourth means "next after third"   *Forth* means "forward"

1. The players ran back and _____ across the gym.

_____ means _____

2. Jerome was _____ in line for ice cream.

_____ means _____

Complete the sentences using *knew* **or** *new*.
Then write the meaning of the homophone.

Knew means "did know"   *New* means "not old"

3. The _____ theater opened yesterday.

_____ means _____

4. My friends _____ it opened before I did.

_____ means _____

▶**Homophones**

Practice

Use these homophones to complete the sentences. The first one is done for you.

see	piece	knew	meat
sea	peace	new	meet

5. The <u>fourth</u> drummer marched back and <u>forth</u>.

6. Whales swam across the _____.

7. I could _____ the coral reef underwater.

8. This puzzle is missing a _____.

9. Presidents from many countries signed the _____ treaty.

10. My dog _____ the mail carrier was coming.

11. The poodle was proud of the _____ bow in its fur.

12. Many people like vegetables better than _____.

13. Football teams _____ in a huddle.

VOCABULARY

Homophones

Word List

1. two
2. sea
3. rode
4. road
5. meet
6. meat

Selection Words

7. to
8. see
9. piece
10. fourth

Pattern Study

▶Write the spelling word that sounds the same as each word, but is spelled differently.

1. peace _____

2. meat _____

3. see _____

4. forth _____

5. two _____

6. sea _____

7. rode _____

8. to _____

9. road _____

10. meet _____

▶**Homophones**

Strategies

 Meaning Strategy Complete the sentences below with the correct spelling word.

11. meet or **meat**   The sandwich had _____, lettuce, and a tomato.

12. see or **sea**   A lighthouse sat by the _____.

13. road or **rode**   We _____ the bus to the football game.

14. see or **sea**   It was foggy and hard to _____.

15. road or **rode**   A car traveled on the _____.

16. meet or **meat**   Our grandparents will _____ us at the train station.

17. peace or **piece**   I would love a _____ of pie.

18. fourth or **forth**   Wednesday is the _____ day of the week.

19. two or **to**   Homophones are _____ words that sound alike.

20. two or **to**   I would like _____ know the answer.

SPELLING

▶Homographs

> **Homographs** are words that have the same spelling, but different pronunciations and meanings.
>
> | **presents** | gifts | introduces, gives |
> |---|---|---|
> | **sow** | plant seeds | female pig |
> | **address** | where someone lives | speak to |

 Try It! **Write the meaning of the underlined word. Then pronounce the word.**

1. The new mother received <u>presents</u> for her new baby.

   presents means: _____

2. The <u>address</u> of the White House is 1600 Pennsylvania Avenue.

   address means: _____

3. I will <u>sow</u> pumpkin seeds this spring.

   sow means: _____

4. The mayor will <u>address</u> the people later tonight.

   address means: _____

5. Our <u>sow</u> loved to roll around in the mud.

   sow means: _____

Homographs • Spelling and Vocabulary Skills

UNIT 6 Our Country and Its People • **Lesson 5** *The Butterfly Seeds*

▶ **Homographs**

Practice

Use the homographs below to complete the sentences. Use each word more than once. Say each word aloud as you write it in the sentence.

close   presents   address   sow

6. The _____ snorted and ate the apples.

7. Please _____ the refrigerator to save energy.

8. My home _____ is 135 Maple Street.

9. A teacher _____ new students to the class.

10. Do not forget to _____ the door after yourself.

11. A farmer may _____ corn in the spring.

12. I will _____ the queen as "Your Majesty."

13. There were many _____ for the students at the party.

14. I came _____ to being hit with a baseball.

VOCABULARY

▶ Homographs

Word List

1. read
2. live
3. dove
4. lead
5. sow
6. does
7. tear
8. wind

Selection Words

9. close
10. presents

Pattern Study

▶Write the spelling words that can rhyme with the words given below.

     red   said

1. _____

2. _____

find

3. _____

give

4. _____

love

5. _____

nose

6. _____

bow

7. _____

UNIT 6 Our Country and Its People • **Lesson 5** *The Butterfly Seeds*

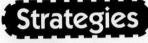

▶**Homographs**

SPELLING

Strategies

Meaning Strategy Write the spelling word from the box that fits twice in each sentence. The first one is done for you.

| lead | wind | sow | tear | dove | presents |

8. A farmer may <u>sow</u> seed and feed his <u>sow</u>.

9. The _____ scientist in the group studied

_____ and silver.

10. The school _____ nice _____ to a birthday child.

11. The blowing _____ began to _____ the kite string around the tree.

12. The _____ swiftly _____ for the birdseed on the sidewalk.

13. The baby cried a _____ because his stuffed

animal had a _____.

UNIT 6 Our Country and Its People • **Lesson 6** *A Piece of Home*

▶ Multicultural Words

A **garmoshka** is a musical instrument with round buttons played by squeezing.

We use the word **garmoshka** because this instrument came from Russia, where the instrument was named in the Russian language.

 **Try It!** Fill in each blank of these sentences from "A Piece of Home" with one of the words in the box.

garmoshka	samovar	Russian	bureau

1. Papa says, "I must take my _____, for how could I live in America without music?"

2. Mama says, "I will take our small _____. My

   sister Marissa always loved our good _____ tea."

3. On Mama's _____ is a picture of cousin Elie.

UNIT 6 Our Country and Its People • **Lesson 6** *A Piece of Home*

▶**Multicultural Words**

Practice

In the story, the family is from Russia. They are a **Russian** family. The ending *-n* on the word *Russian* means "of" or "from." The ending *-ian* also means "of" or "from."

Add *-n* to the following place names to create words that mean "of" or "from" that place. Begin each new word with a capital letter.

4. Russia   +   n = _____

5. Korea   +   n = _____

6. India   +   n = _____

7. Jamaica +   n = _____

Drop the underlined letter or letters and add *-ian* to the following place names to create words that mean "of" or "from" that place.

8. Cana<u>da</u>   + ian = _____

9. Ital<u>y</u>   + ian = _____

10. Colomb<u>ia</u> + ian = _____

VOCABULARY

▶ Words with Foreign Origins

Word List

1. nickel
2. pretzel
3. pinto
4. burro
5. bronco
6. siesta
7. fiesta
8. buffet
9. beret
10. ballet

Pattern Study

Look at the patterns:

yode**l**   chale**t**   sil**o**   sals**a**

▶ Write the spelling words spelled like *yodel*.

1. _____   2. _____

▶ Write the spelling words spelled like *chalet*.

3. _____   5. _____

4. _____

▶ Write the spelling words spelled like *silo*.

6. _____   8. _____

7. _____

▶ Write the spelling words spelled like *salsa*.

9. _____   10. _____

UNIT 6 Our Country and Its People • **Lesson 6** *A Piece of Home*

▶ **Words with Foreign Origins**

Strategies

Foreign Language Strategy Write the spelling words from French that end with the same sound as *way* and *stay*.

11. _____

12. _____

13. _____

Write the spelling words from Spanish that end with the same sound as *fellow* and *yellow*.

14. _____

15. _____

16. _____

Dictionary Strategy Fill in the spelling word that matches the meaning. A dictionary may help.

17. A coin worth five cents is a _____.

18. A snack shaped like a knot is a _____.

19. An afternoon rest or nap is a _____.

20. A holiday or festival is a _____.

SPELLING

Name _____ Date _____

▶Review

A **homophone** is a word that has the same sound as another word, but it has a different spelling and meaning.

 **Try It!** **Complete the sentence using *fourth* or *forth*. Then write the meaning of the word.**

Fourth means "next after third"   *Forth* means "forward"

1. The boat tossed back and _____ on the waves.

_____ means _____

2. I will be in _____ grade after I finish third.

_____ means _____

Complete the sentences using *peace* or *piece*. Then write the meaning of the word.

Peace means "not fighting"   *Piece* means "part"

3. The boys were at _____ and no longer angry.

_____ means _____

4. I lost a _____ of the puzzle.

_____ means _____

Practice

Use these homophones to complete the sentences.

dough	kneads	for	eight	poor
doe	needs	four	ate	pour

5. I _____ a huge piece of pie.

6. There are _____ legs on an octopus.

7. The server will _____ a glass of lemonade.

8. College costs a lot of money, so the student was

   _____.

9. A female deer is called a _____.

10. Gingerbread _____ smells good, but it is very rich.

11. Sign up _____ the team in the gym.

12. A square has _____ corners.

13. The animal _____ food and water.

14. An artist _____ clay before using it.

▶ Review

Word List

1. peace
2. forth
3. eight
4. four
5. into
6. notebook

Selection Words

7. turnovers
8. something
9. everything
10. whatever

Pattern Study

▶ Write a spelling word that sounds the same as each word, but is spelled differently.

1. piece _____

2. fourth _____

3. ate _____

4. for _____

▶ Combine the words below to form spelling words.

5. some + thing = _____

6. what + ever = _____

7. every + thing = _____

8. in + to = _____

9. turn + overs = _____

10. note + book = _____

UNIT 6 Our Country and Its People • **Lesson 7** *Jalapeño Bagels*

▶**Review**

Strategies

 Conventions Strategy Match the words to form a spelling word. Then write the spelling word on the line. The first one is done for you.

11. some   to

    something

12. every   thing

_____

13. turn   overs

_____

14. what   thing

_____

15. in   ever

_____

16. note   book

_____

SPELLING

►Vocabulary Rules

Synonyms are words that are similar in meaning.

The solution to the puzzle is **easy.**
The solution to the puzzle is **simple.**

Antonyms are words that are opposite in meaning.

An elephant is a **large** animal.
A mouse is a **small** animal.

Homophones are words that are pronounced alike but are spelled differently and have different meanings.

The wind **blew** white clouds across the **blue** sky.
They're happy that **their** team won over **there.**
You're sure **your** team won?
It's a shame that the tree lost **its** leaves so soon.

Word Roots A word root is the main part of a word. Sometimes a prefix or suffix is added to it. These additions often change a word's meaning or its part of speech.

Audio means "hear."

An **audiotape** is a tape you **listen** to.
An **audience** is a group that **hears** a performance.
Audiovisual materials help us to see and **hear** what we are learning.

Prefixes and Suffixes

- **Prefixes** are word parts added to the beginning of a root that change its meaning.

  A **co**worker is a person that one works with.
  To **co**write is to write together.

- **Suffixes** are word parts added to the end of a root that change its meaning.

  Fear**ful** means "full of fear."
  A spoon**ful** is the amount that fills a spoon.

VOCABULARY

▶Spelling Strategies

There are many different ways to learn how to spell. A spelling strategy is a plan that can make learning to spell easier. Take some time to learn how these strategies can help you spell better.

Sound Pattern Strategies

Pronunciation Strategy
Learn to listen to the sounds in a word. Then spell each sound. *(sit)*

Consonant-Substitution Strategy
Try switching consonant letters without changing the vowel. *(bat, hat, rat, flat)*

Vowel-Substitution Strategy
Try switching the vowel letters without changing the rest of the word. *(hit, hat, hut, hot) / (mane, mine) / (boat, beat)*

Rhyming Strategy
Think of a word that rhymes with the spelling word and has the same spelling pattern. *(cub, tub, rub)*

Structural Pattern Strategies

Conventions Strategy

Think about the rules and exceptions you have learned for adding endings to words. (*crying, cried*)

Visualization Strategy

Think about how the word looks. Most words look wrong when they do not have the right spelling. (*can,* not *cen*)

Proofreading Strategy

Check your writing carefully for spelling mistakes.

Meaning Pattern Strategies

Meaning Strategy

Think about the meaning of the word to make sure you're using the right word. (*see, sea*)

Compound Word Strategy

Break the compound into its two words to spell each word. (*homework, home work*)

Foreign Language Strategy

Think of foreign word spellings that are different from English spelling patterns. (*ballet*)

Dictionary Strategy

Find the word in a dictionary to make sure your spelling is correct.

Spelling Rules

General Spelling Rules for Most Words

- All words have at least one vowel.

- Most words have at least one consonant.

- Every syllable has a vowel or the letter *y*.

- Many words are spelled exactly as they sound.

- Some words are exceptions to spelling rules and must be memorized.

Consonant Spellings

Most consonants sound like their letter names.

- /b/ is spelled *b* as in *bad*
- /d/ is spelled *d* as in *dash*
- /f/ is spelled *f* as in *fast*
- /j/ is spelled *j* as in *jog*
- /k/ is spelled *k* as in *kiss*
- /l/ is spelled *l* as in *lot*
- /m/ is spelled *m* as in *map*
- /n/ is spelled *n* as in *nest*
- /p/ is spelled *p* as in *pin*
- /r/ is spelled *r* as in *rug*
- /s/ is spelled *s* as in *sand*
- /t/ is spelled *t* as in *tip*
- /v/ is spelled *v* as in *vat*
- /z/ is spelled *z* as in *zip*

SPELLING

Consonant Spellings (continued)

Some consonants do not sound like their letter names.

- /h/ does not sound like the letter *h*.   *(hill)*

- /w/ does not sound like the letter *w*.   *(wish)*

- /y/ does not sound like the letter *y*.   *(yell)*

- There are hard and soft sounds for the letter *c*.
  hard *c*: /k/ is spelled *c* as in *can*
  soft *c*: /s/ is spelled *c* as in *cell*

- There are hard and soft sounds for the letter *g*.
  hard *g*: /g/ is spelled *g* as in *gum*
  soft *g*: /j/ is spelled *g* as in *gym*

- The /ks/ as in *ax* or the /gz/ as in *exact* are
  both spelled with the letter *x*.